Green Eyes

Green Eyes sleeps in a box
in our classroom, but not
when the teacher's looking.

Green Eyes tries to catch the parrot,

but not when the teacher's looking.

Green Eyes scratches me
when I walk through the door,

6

but not when the teacher's looking.

Green Eyes jumps all over the paintings

but not when the teacher's looking.

Green Eyes sharpens her claws on the curtains,

but not when the teacher's looking.

Green Eyes sneaks some of
Gino's lunch,

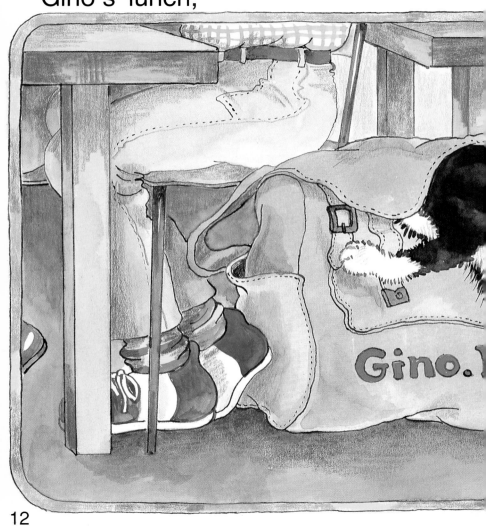

but not when the teacher's looking.

Green Eyes hides
in the arts and crafts boxes,

but not when the teacher's looking.

Our teacher doesn't like Green Eyes.
I bet she loves kittens, though.